BASTIEN PIANO BASICS



# Theory & Technic for the Young Beginner

## PRIMER B

BY JAMES BASTIEN

70¢

## Contents



*To reinforce the feeling of achievement, the teacher or student may put a ✓ when the page has been mastered.

ISBN 0-8497-9320-3

# Middle C Position

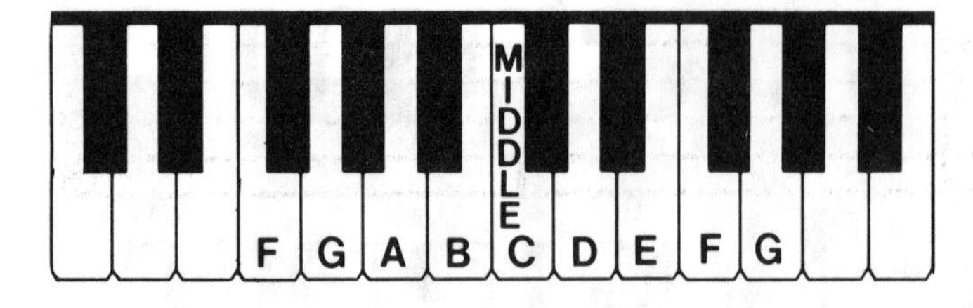


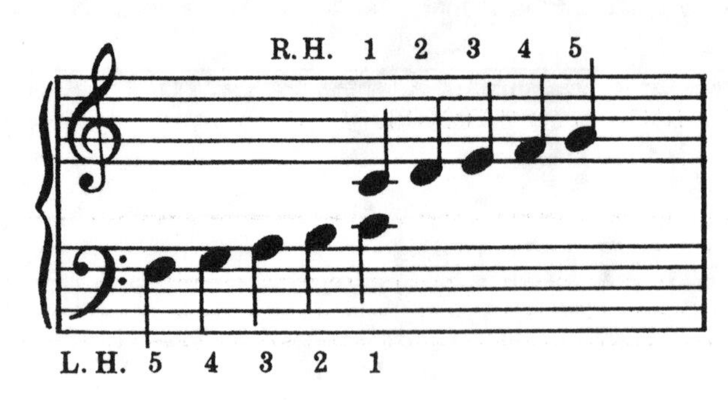

1. Draw quarter notes in the middle C position. Play and name these notes.

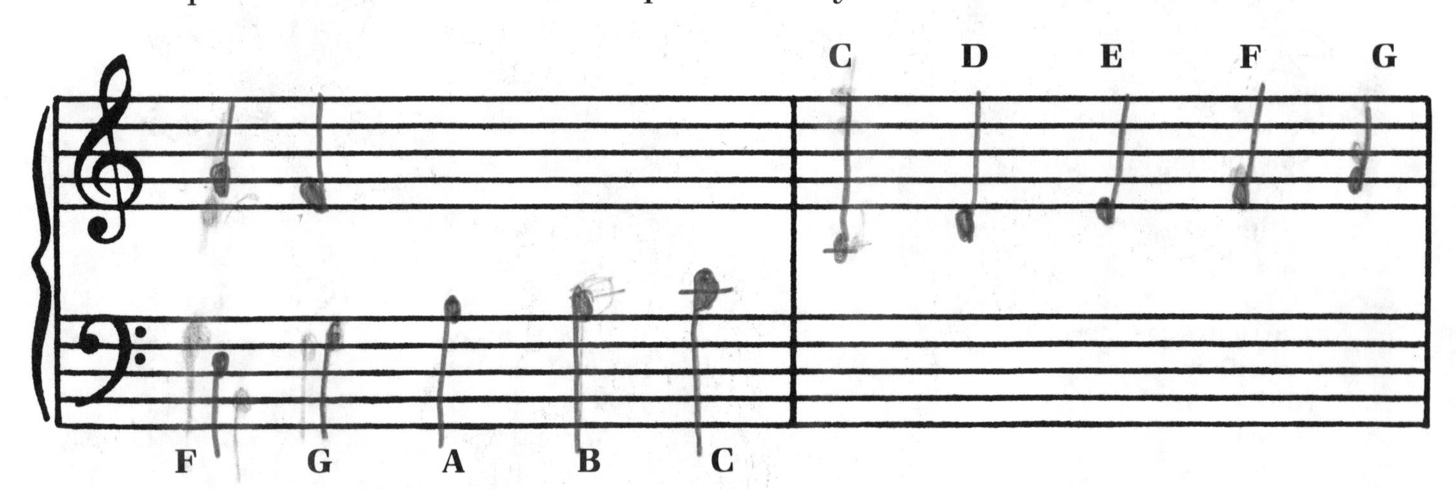


# Note-Spelling Fun!

2. Write the letter names of these notes to spell words.
   Play and name these notes in the middle C position.

**3.** Draw these notes. Use quarter notes. Play and name these notes.

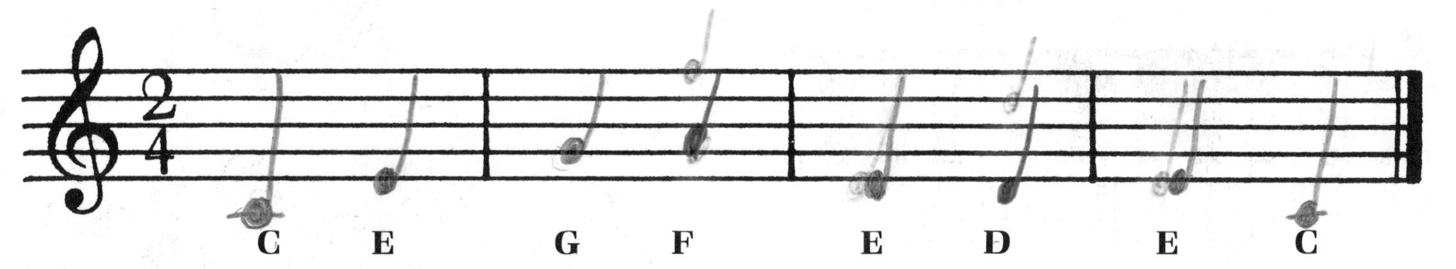


**4.** Draw these notes. Use quarter notes. Play and name these notes.

**5.** Play this music
and name the notes.

## *Cats*

# Two Eighth Notes

**Two eighth notes** equal one quarter note.
They are connected with a **beam**.

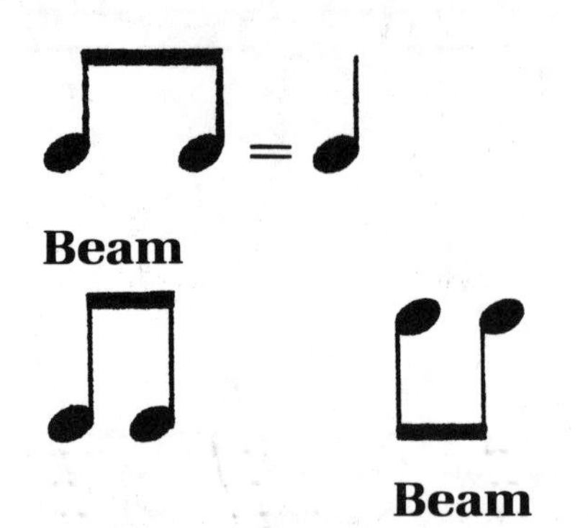
Beam
Beam

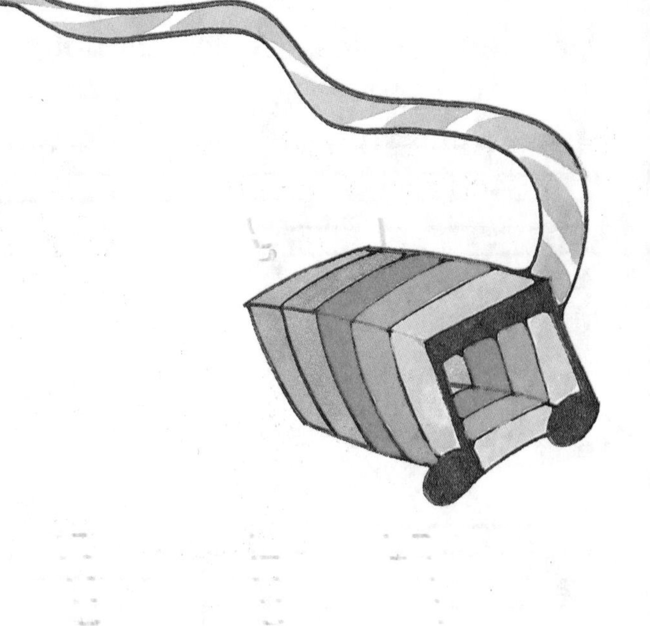

**6.** Add a beam to these pairs of notes to form two eighth notes.

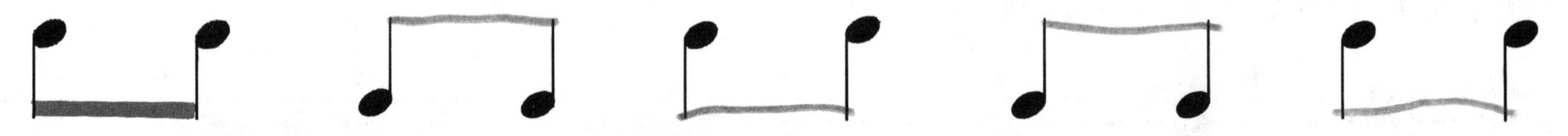

Eighth notes may be counted with numbers by saying *"and"* after the number.

1 and 2 and
1 and 2 and

**7.** Clap and count the following rhythm.

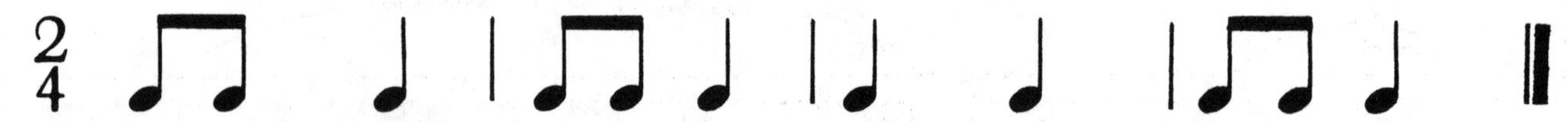

*Count:* 1 and 2 and
*or:* two eighths quar-ter

**8.** Play this music and count aloud.
Use either of the counting systems shown on this page.

## Kites

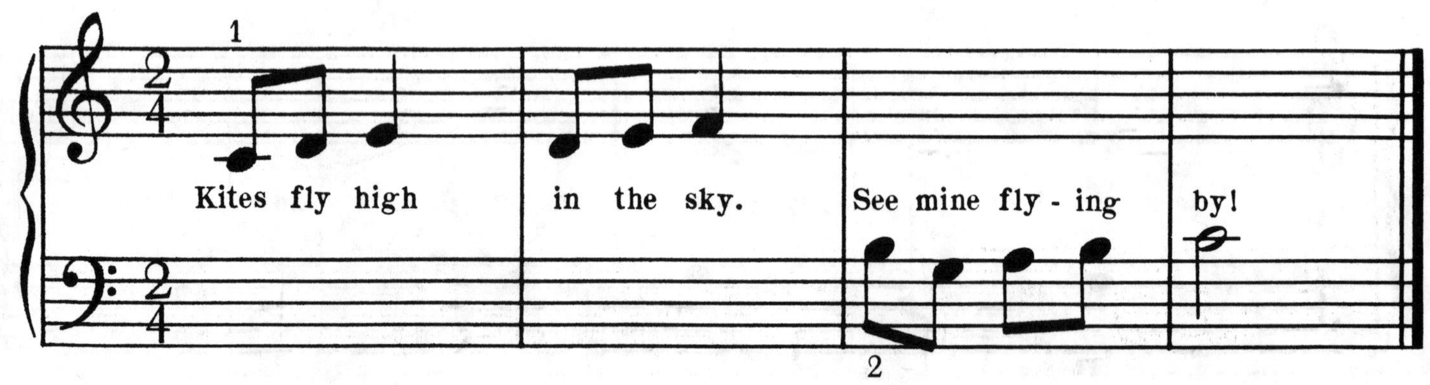
Kites fly high
in the sky.
See mine fly - ing
by!

*Use with page 6 of* Piano for the Young Beginner, *Primer B*.

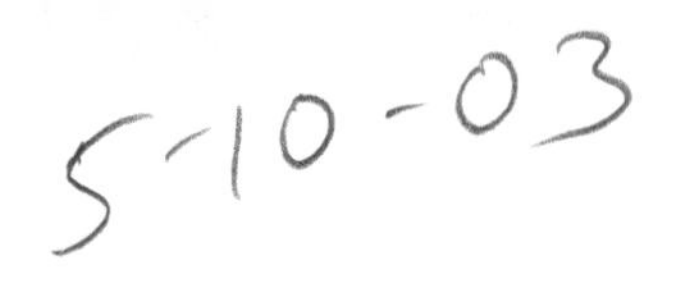



# Technic

**9.** Play this exercise and repeat it several times.

## *Bees in Spring*

**10.** Play this exercise and repeat it several times.

## *The Crawling Caterpillar*

# C Position

Notes **on or above** the middle line have **down stems**.

Notes **below** the middle line have **up stems**.

**11.** Draw the C position notes in the **bass clef** two times.

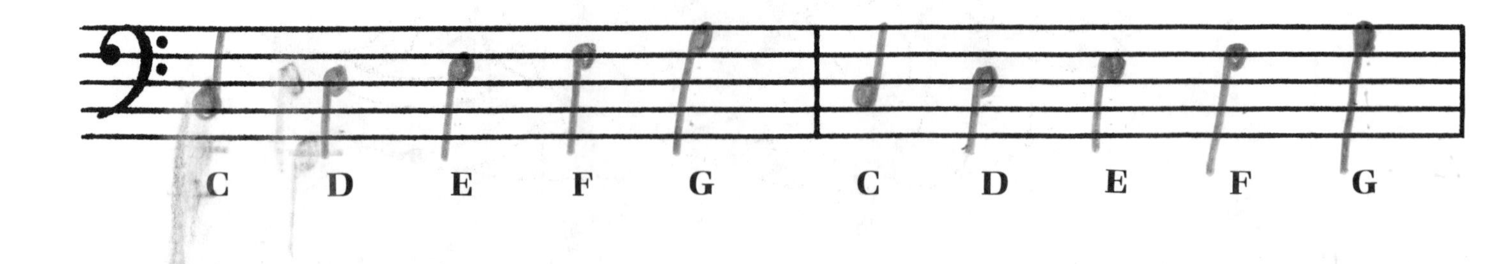


**12.** Draw the C position notes in the **treble clef** two times.

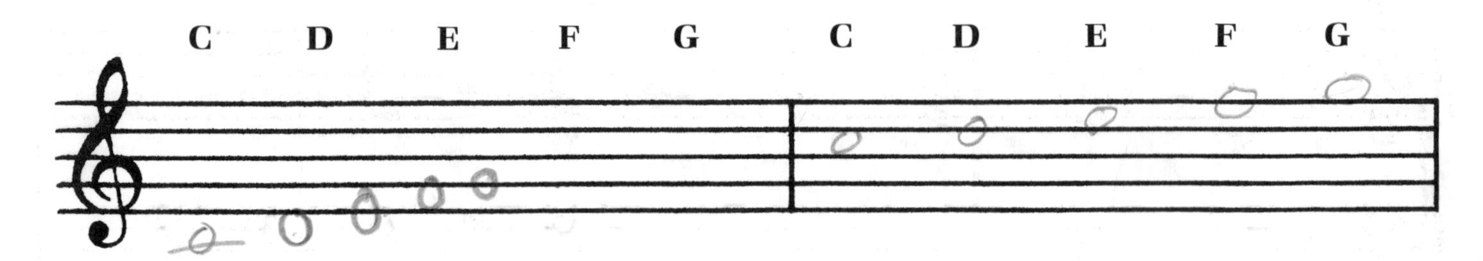


**13.** Write the names of these notes. Play them.

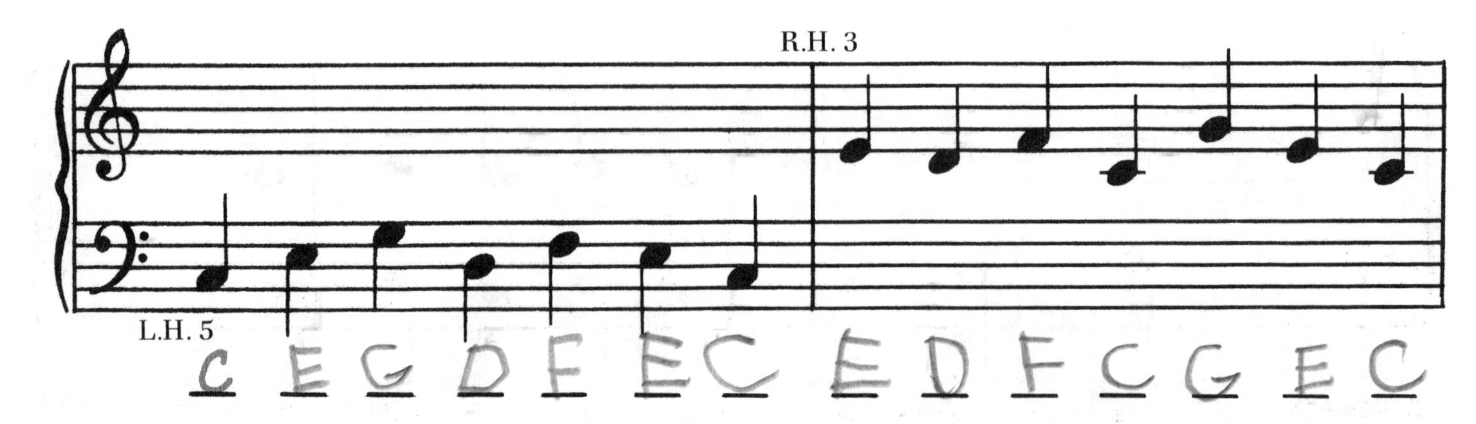




*Use with page 8 of* Piano for the Young Beginner, *Primer B*.

**14.** Play this exercise and repeat it several times. You may play it hands separately first.*

## Workout in C

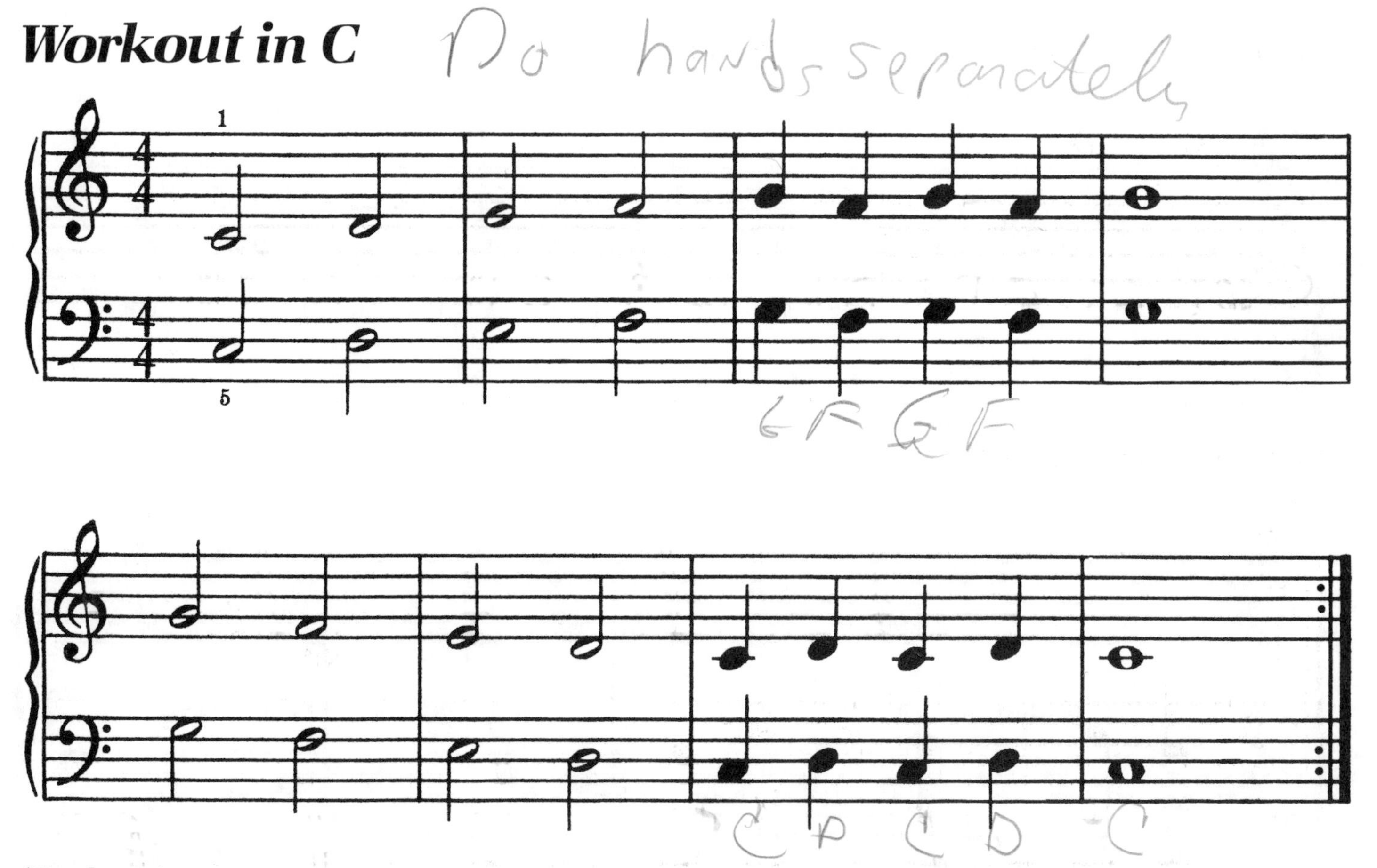

***Teacher:** This practice direction is only a suggestion. You may want the student to begin with both hands.

# Dynamics

Dynamics are **loud** and **soft** signs in music.

***f*** means **loud**.
Its Italian name is ***forte***.

***p*** means **soft**.
Its Italian name is ***piano***.

**15.** Trace the first two ***f*** signs, then draw four more.

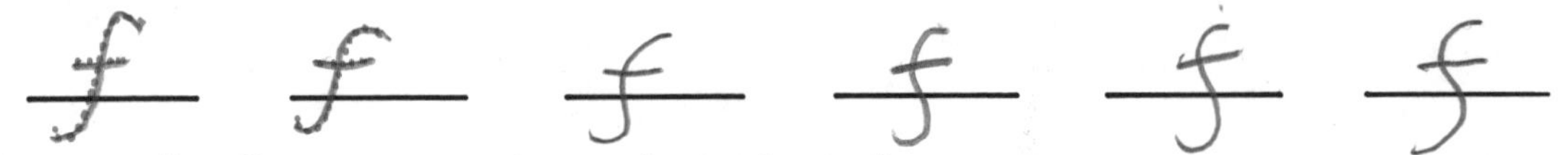

**16.** Trace the first two ***p*** signs, then draw four more.

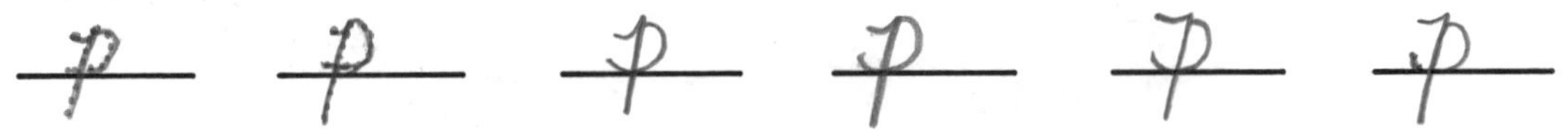

**17.** Read the words of this song. At the beginning of each line, write the dynamic sign that matches the words of that line. Play this piece.

## *Our School Band*

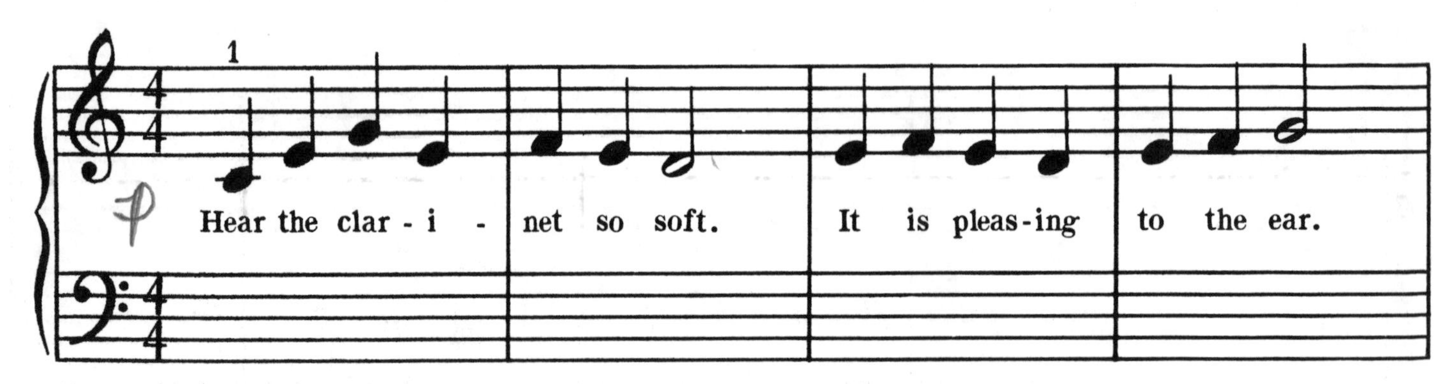


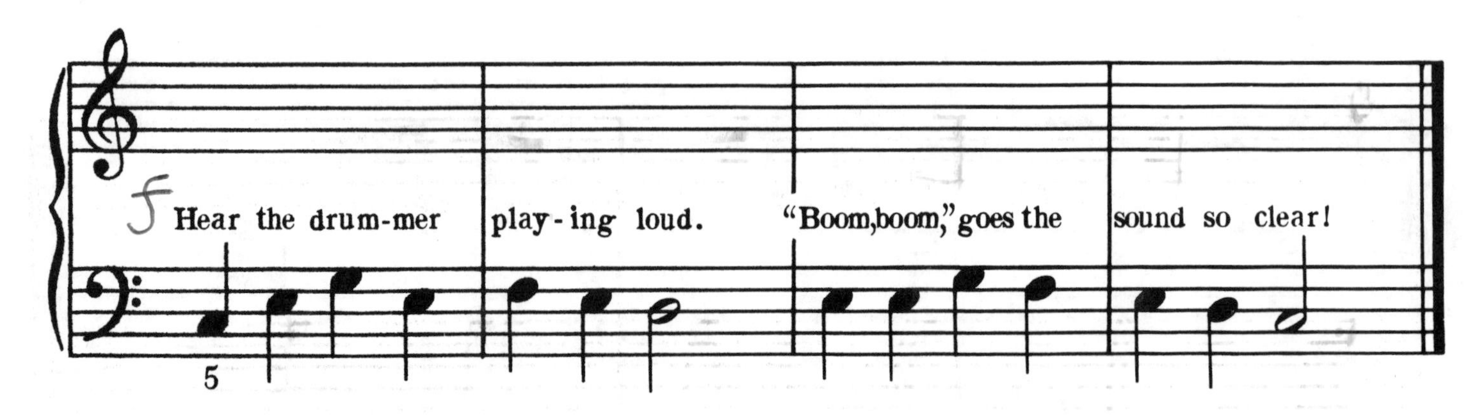




*Use with page 10 of* Piano for the Young Beginner, *Primer B*.

6-16-03

**18.** Play this exercise and repeat it once.
**f-p** means to play first time **f** (loud), the second time **p** (soft).

## *Hear the Wind Blow!*

# Measuring Intervals

**2nd** The distance from one key to the next key is a **2nd**.

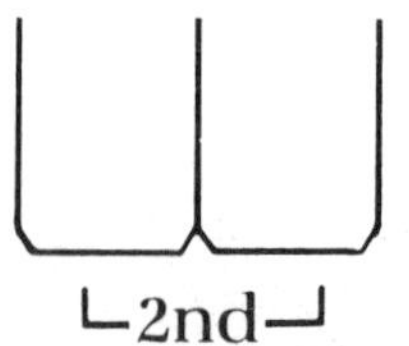


On the staff a 2nd is either line to space or space to line.

**19.** Write an interval of a 2nd **up** from the given letters. Play these intervals on your piano. Use either hand.

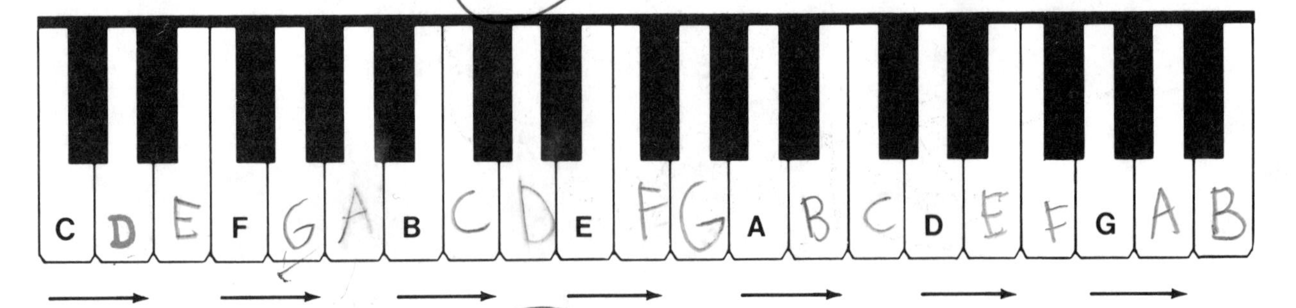


**20.** Write an interval of a 2nd **down** from the given letters. Play these intervals on your piano. Use either hand.

**21.** Draw a note an interval of a 2nd from the given note. Draw the note above if the arrow is up, or below if the arrow is down. Play and name these notes.

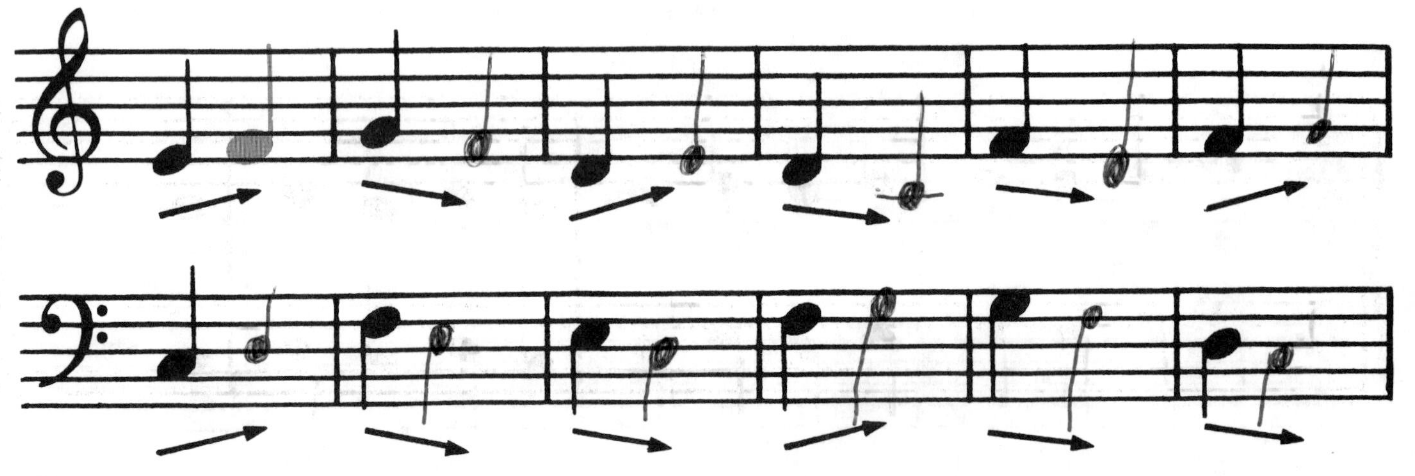



*Use with pages 12-15 of* Piano for the Young Beginner, *Primer B.*

**22.** Play this exercise and repeat it once.

## Monkey Twins

6-16-03

# 3rd

One skipped key is a **3rd**.

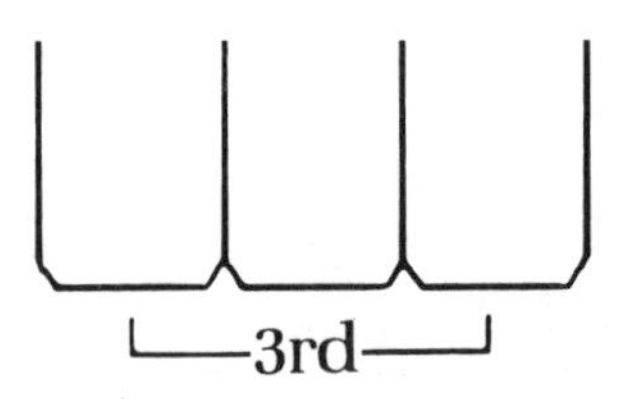


On the staff a 3rd is either line to line or space to space.

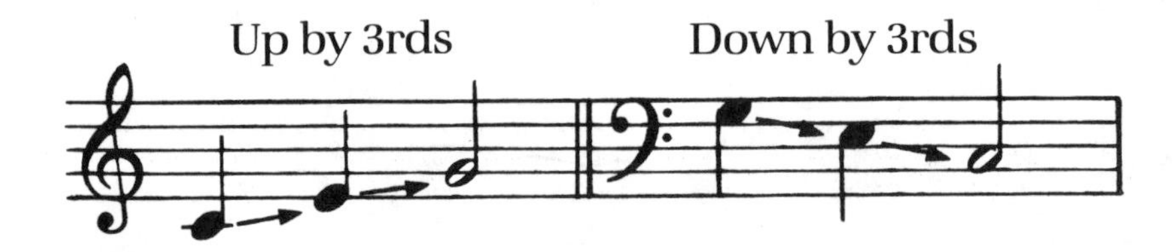


**23.** Write an interval of a 3rd **up** from the given letters. Play these intervals on your piano. Use either hand.

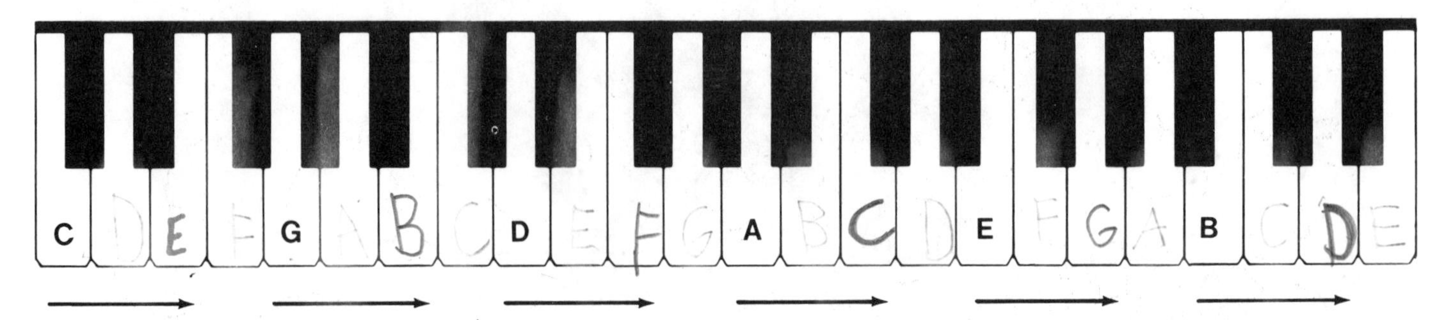


**24.** Write an interval of a 3rd **down** from the given letters. Play these intervals on your piano. Use either hand.

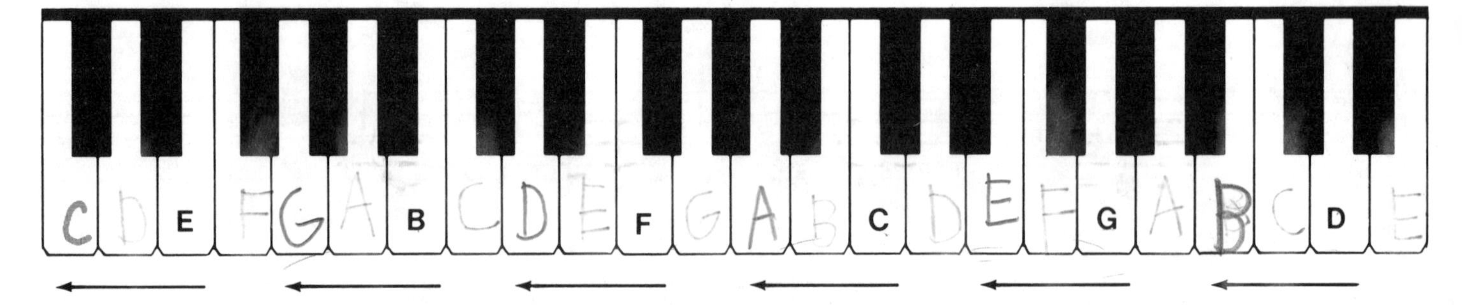


**25.** Draw a note an interval of a 3rd from the given note. Draw the note above if the arrow is up, or below if the arrow is down. Play and name these notes.

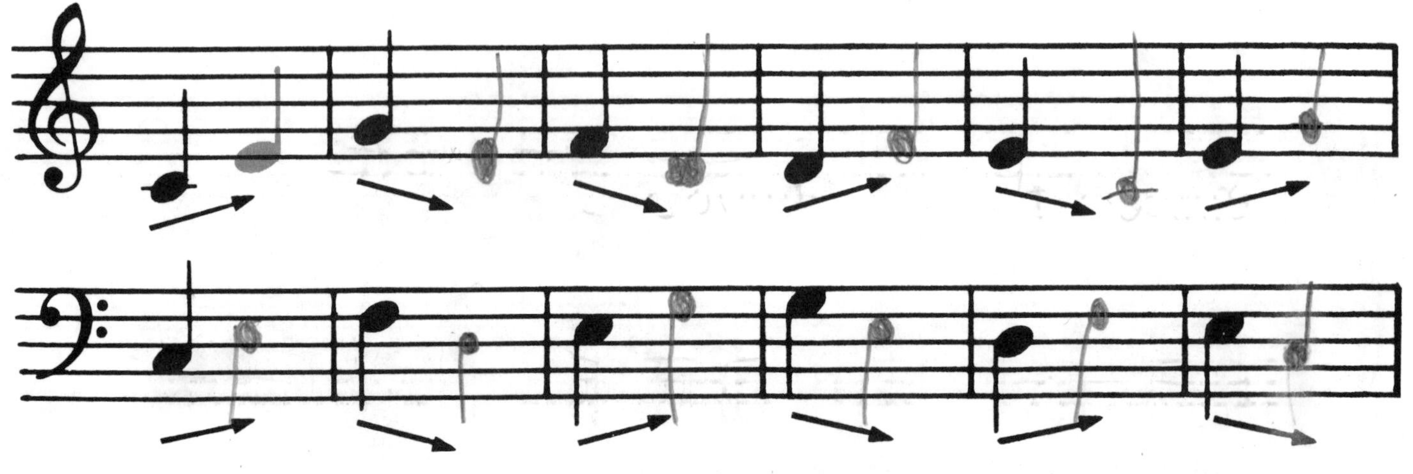



*Use with page 16 of* Piano for the Young Beginner, *Primer B.*

26. Play this exercise and repeat it once.
Three Giraffes
1
f–p
5

# The Slur

The **slur** is a curved line over or under two or more **different** notes that are to be played legato (smooth, connected).

**27.** Draw a slur **over** these notes. Play these notes legato.

Draw a slur **under** these notes. Play these notes legato.

**28.** Draw a slur **under** these notes. Play these notes legato.

# The Tie

The **tie** is a curved line which connects notes that are on the **same** line or space. Play the first note and hold it for the value of both notes.

**29.** Draw a tie to these pairs of same notes. Write the total number of counts for the tied notes on the lines below.

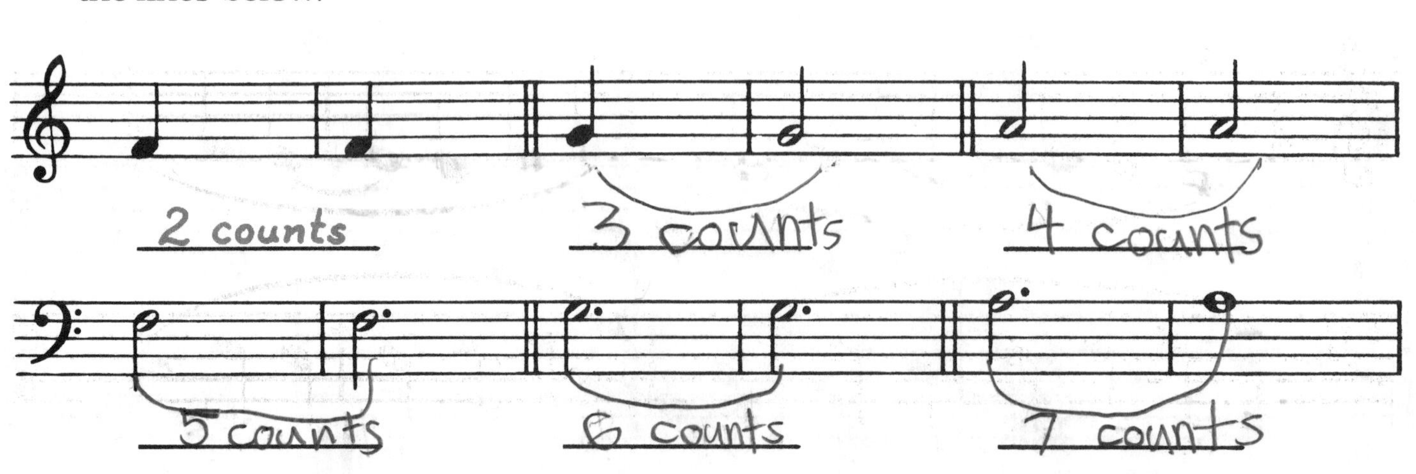




*Use with pages 18-19 of* Piano for the Young Beginner, *Primer B.*

**30.** Lift your hand at the end of each slur with an up wrist motion. Lift on count 3.

## *Lift That Hand!*

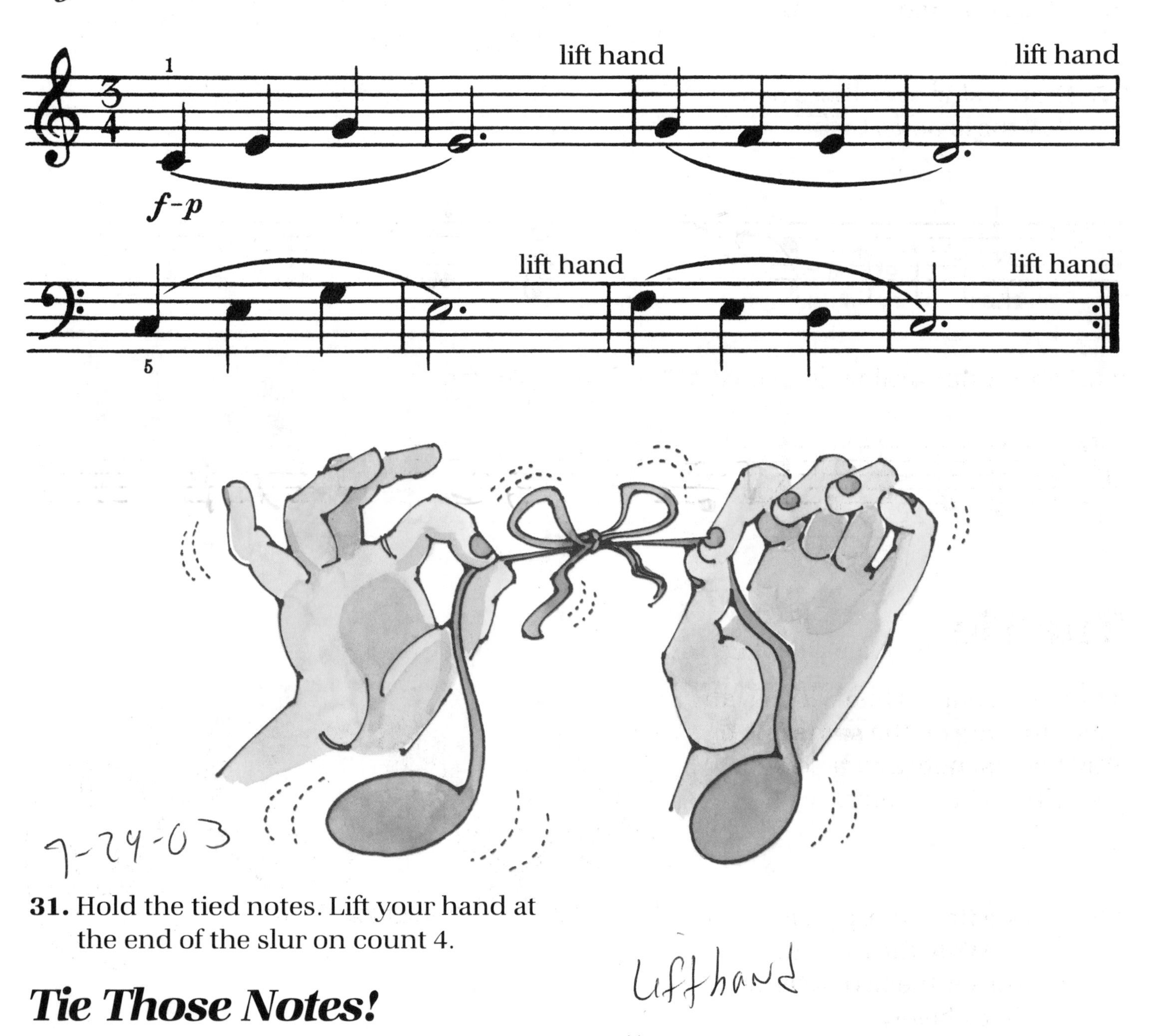


**31.** Hold the tied notes. Lift your hand at the end of the slur on count 4.

## *Tie Those Notes!*

# 4th

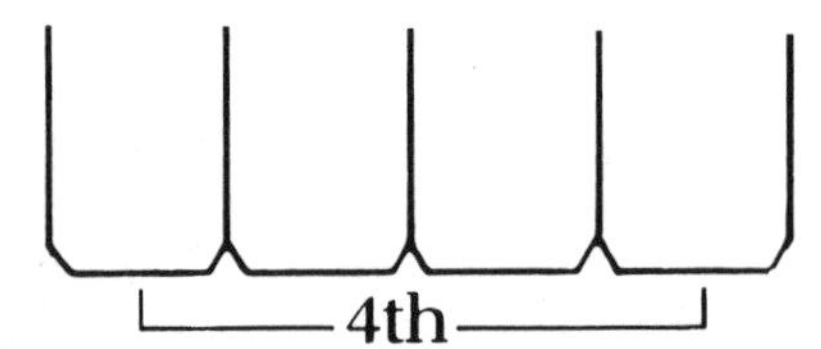


Two skipped keys is a **4th**.

On the staff a 4th is either line to space or space to line.

**32.** Write an interval of a 4th **up** from the given letters.
Play these intervals on your piano. Use either hand.

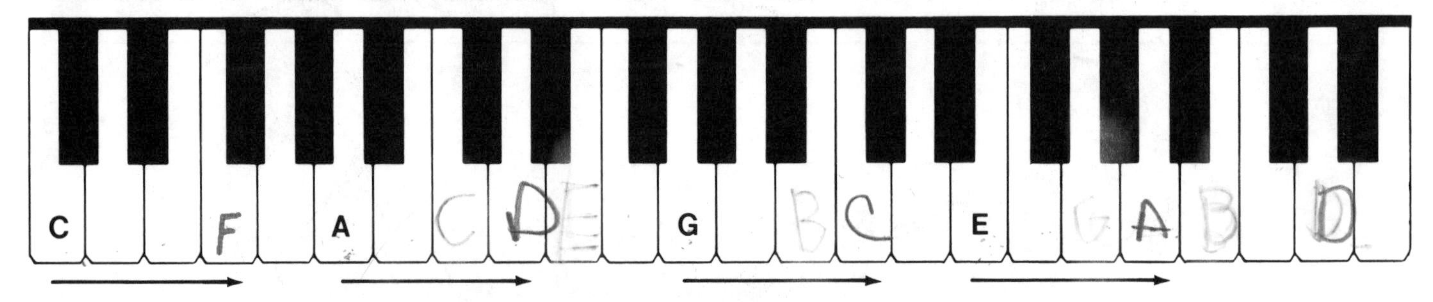


**33.** Write an interval of a 4th **down** from the given letters.
Play these intervals on your piano.

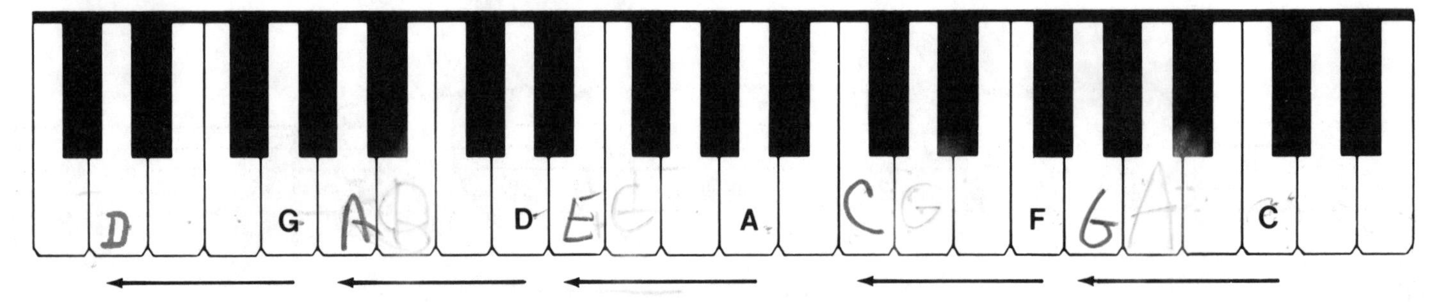


**34.** Write the names of these intervals. Play and name these notes.

*Use with page 20 of* Piano for the Young Beginner, *Primer B.*

**35.** Lift your hand at the end of each slur on count 4.

## *Four Crows*

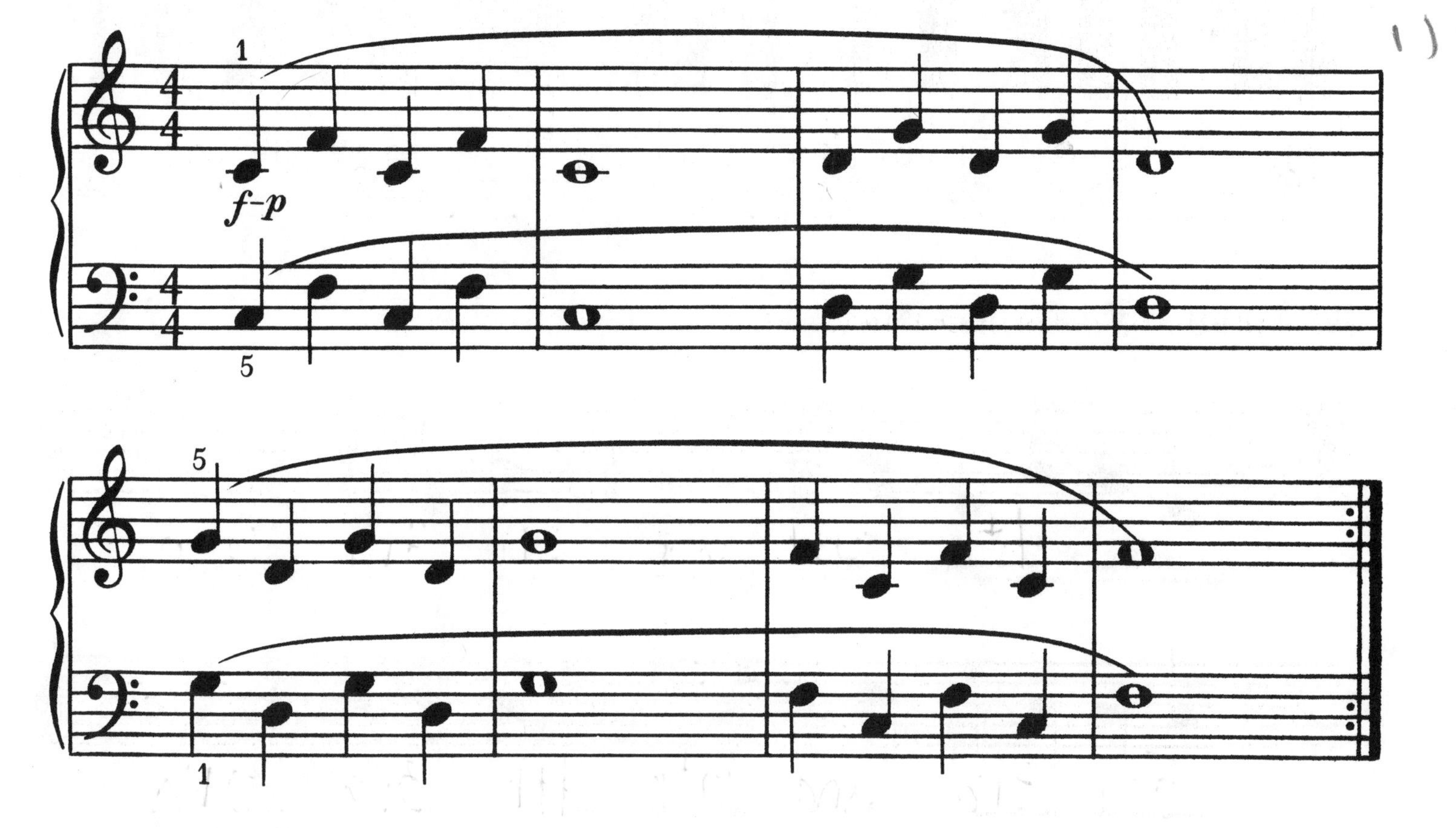

# 5th

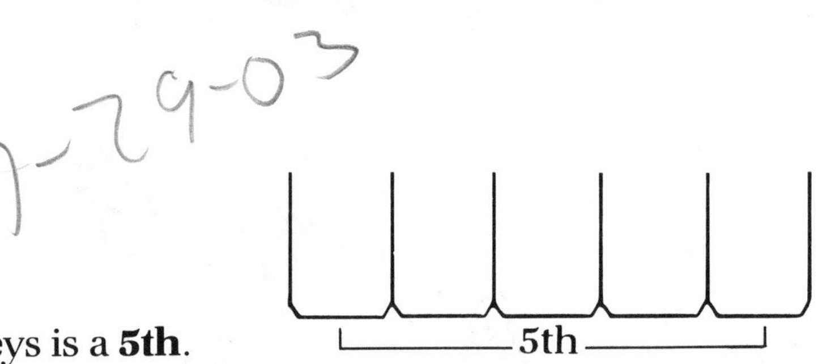


Three skipped keys is a **5th**.

On the staff a 5th is either line to line or space to space.

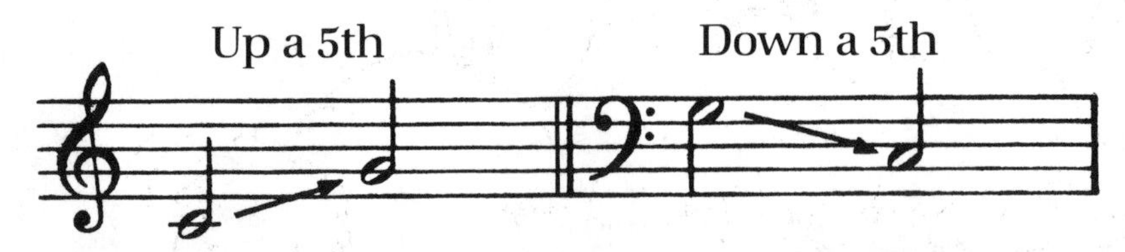


**36.** Write an interval of a 5th **up** from the given letters.
Play these intervals on your piano. Use either hand.

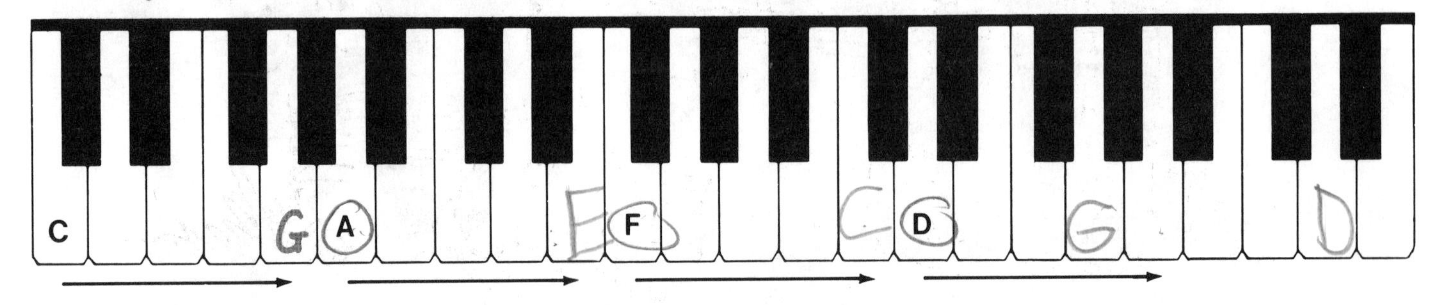


**37.** Write an interval of a 5th **down** from the given letters.
Play these intervals on your piano. Use either hand.

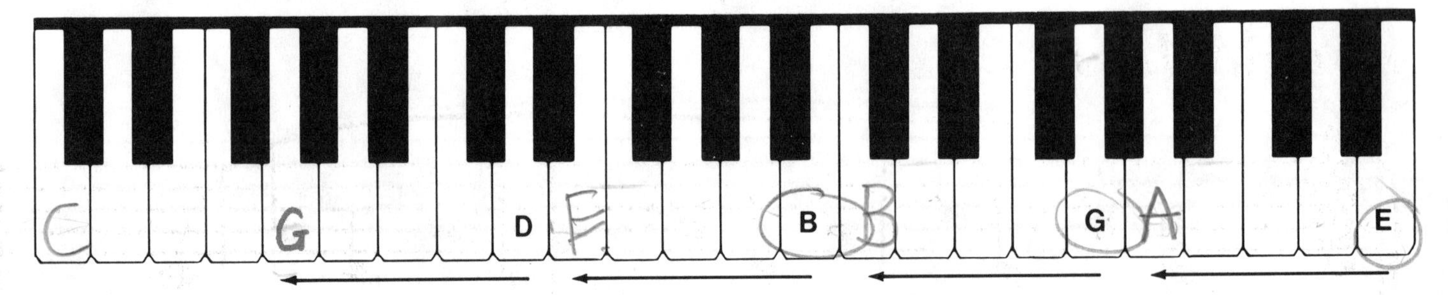


**38.** Write the names of these intervals. Play and name these notes.

*Use with page 24 of* Piano for the Young Beginner, *Primer B.*

39. Lift your hand at the end of the slur on count 4.
Five Rabbits
f-p

# Whole Rest

A **whole rest** lasts for the whole measure.
A rest is used for **silence**.

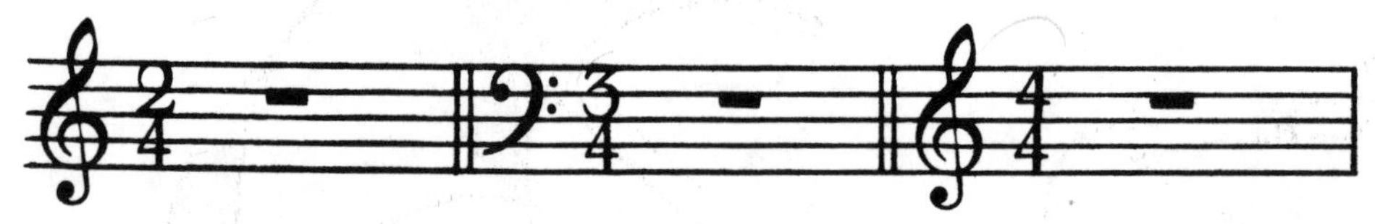

Rest 2 counts Rest 3 counts Rest 4 counts

**40.** Fill in the first two whole rests, then draw four more.
Draw the whole rests hanging down from the **4th line**.

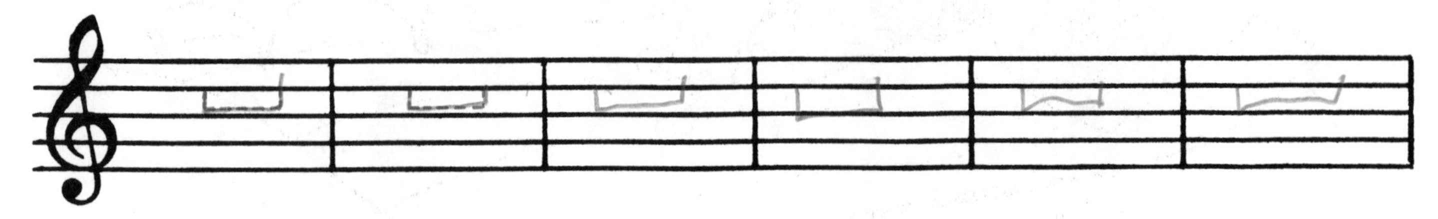

**41.** Draw six whole rests.

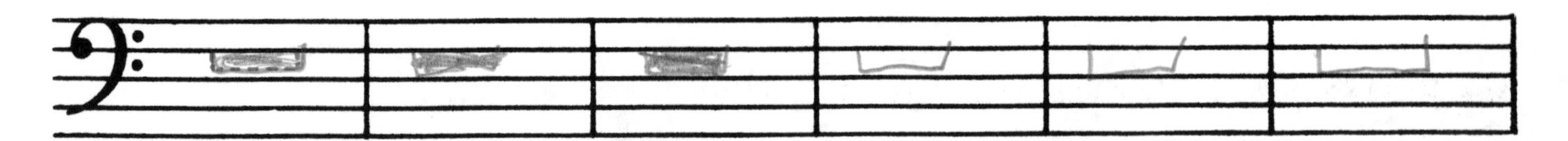

**42.** Draw a whole rest in each measure.
Write the number of counts for each whole rest.

**43.** Draw whole rests in this melody to complete the correct number of beats in each measure.

*Use with page 26 of* Piano for the Young Beginner, *Primer B.*

**44.** Rest 4 counts in the last measure of each line.

## *Take a Rest!*

# Sharp Sign

The **sharp sign** before a note means to play the next key to the **right**.

**45.** Trace the first two sharp signs, then draw four more.
First draw two lines down.
Next, draw two heavy lines across.

The "square" in the middle of the sharp is placed

on a **line** or in a **space**.

**46.** Draw a sharp before each note. Play and name these notes.

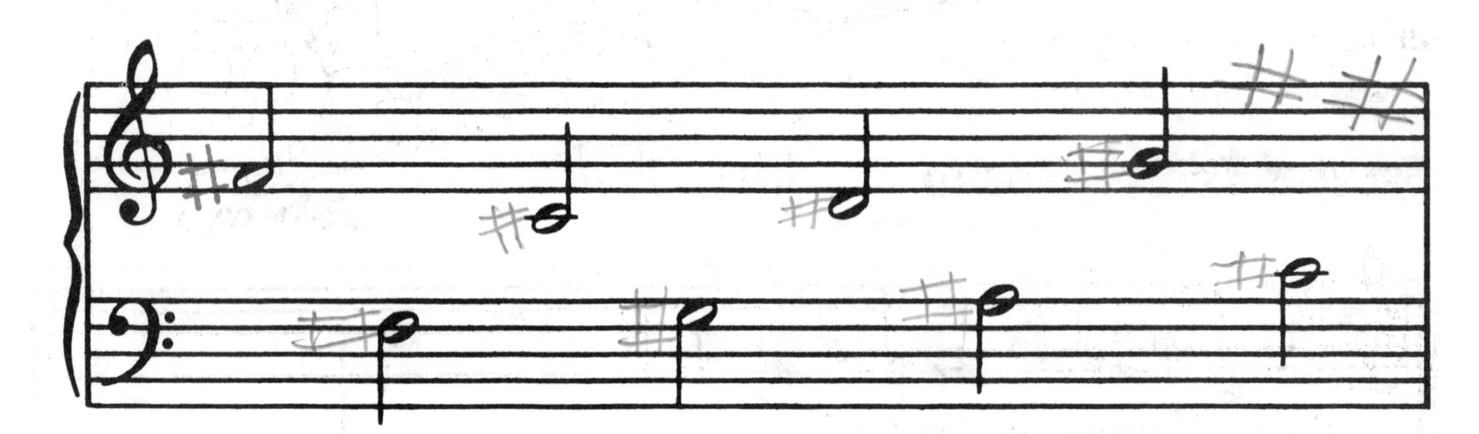

**47.** Draw a sharp before each note with a ♯ sign over it. Play and name these notes.

*Use with page 28 of* Piano for the Young Beginner, *Primer B.*

**48.** Write the names of these sharp keys. Play them.

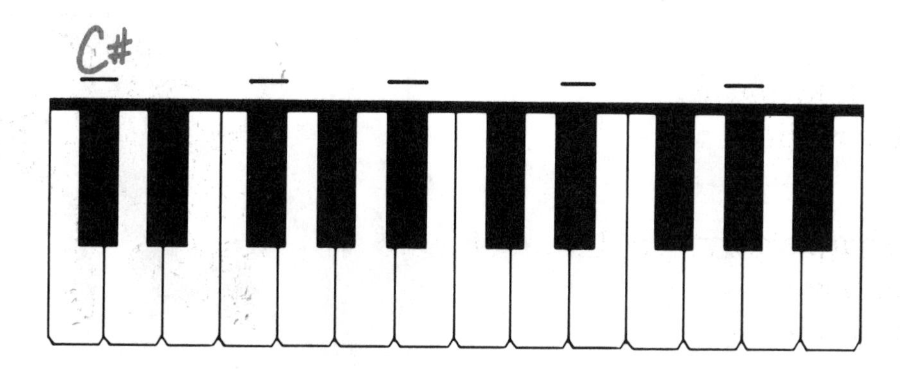


The sharp sign lasts for the **whole** measure.

(also F♯)

**49.** Remember to play F♯ again in each measure where F♯ is used.

## *On the Teeter-Totter*

# Melodic and Harmonic Intervals

**Melodic intervals** are single notes played one at a time, like notes in a melody.

**Harmonic intervals** are two notes played together to make harmony in music.

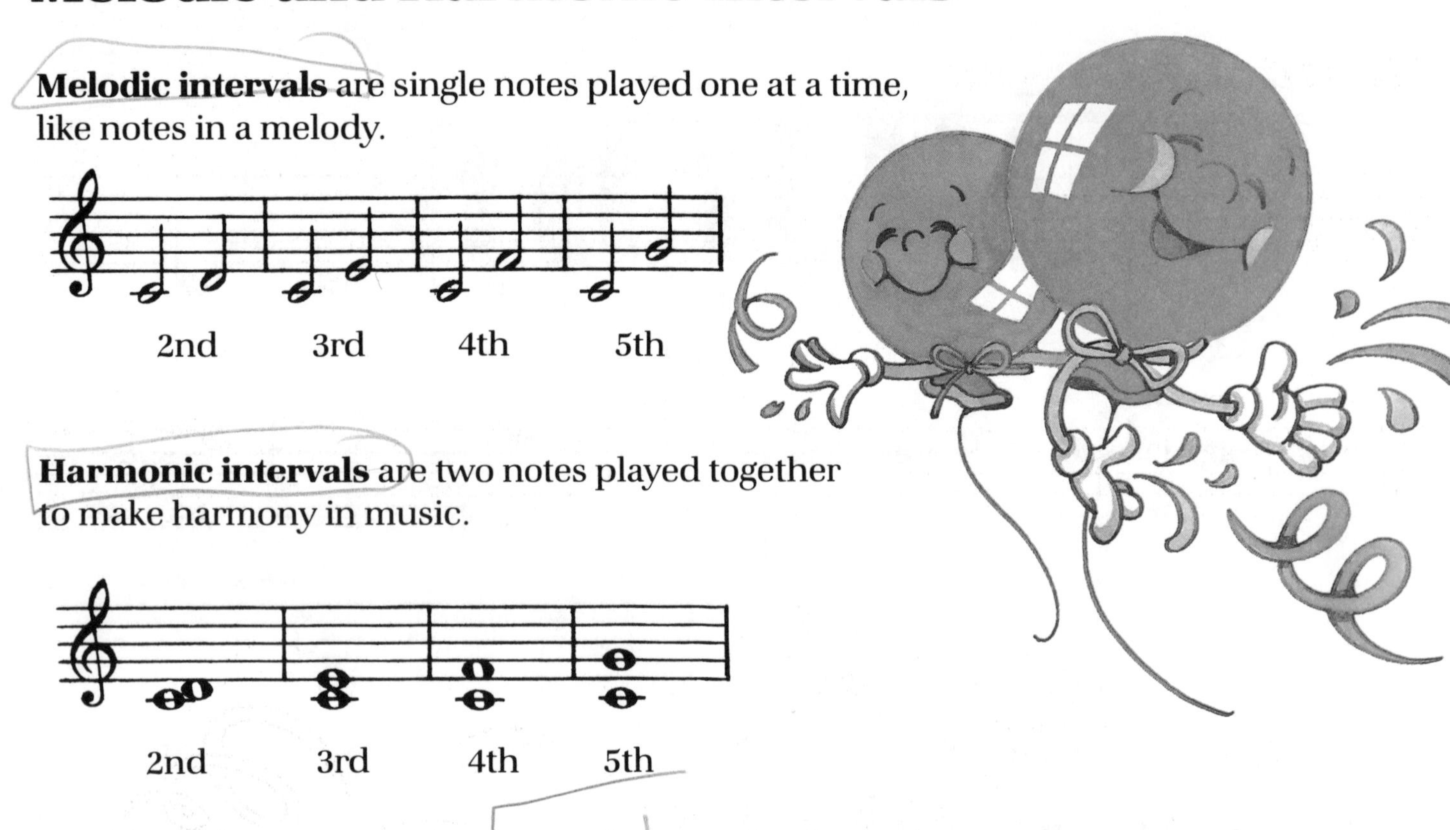


**50.** Write the names of these melodic intervals. Play and name these intervals.

**51.** Draw a half note after the one given to form a melodic interval. Play them.

**52.** Write the names of these harmonic intervals. Play them.

**53.** Draw a whole note above the one given to form a harmonic interval. Play them.

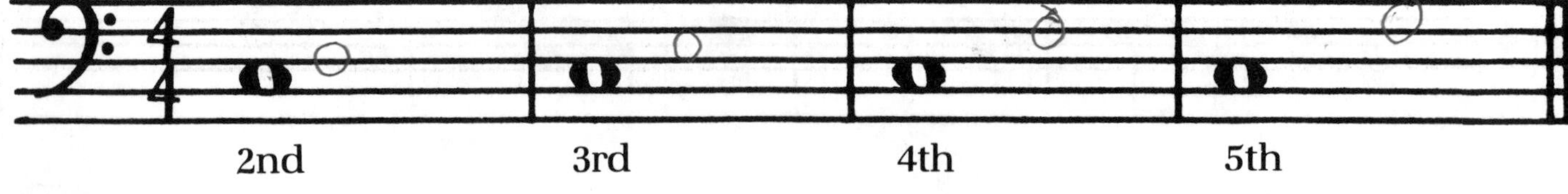




*Use with page 30 of* Piano for the Young Beginner, *Primer B*.

**54.** Play and name the intervals on this page.

## *Melodic Intervals*

## *Harmonic Intervals*

8-26-03

# Quarter Rest 𝄽

A **quarter rest** lasts for the value of a quarter note.

Quarter note ♩ = 1 count
Quarter rest 𝄽 = 1 count

**55.** Trace the first two quarter rests, then draw four more.

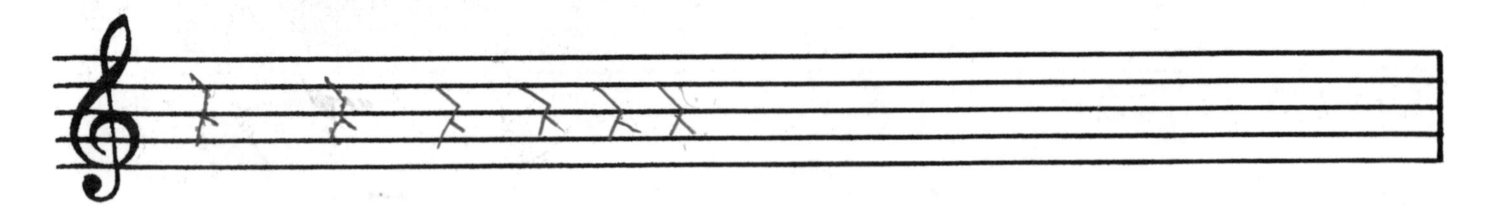

**56.** Draw quarter rests in this melody to complete the correct number of beats in each measure.

**57.** Draw quarter rests in this melody to complete the correct number of beats in each measure.

**58.** Draw quarter rests in this melody to complete the correct number of beats in each measure.

*Use with page 31 of* Piano for the Young Beginner, *Primer B.*

59. These intervals
may also be played
in groups of 3's and 4's.
Clip-Clop Trail
f-p
Echo Canyon
f
p
f
p

# Staccato Notes

**Staccato notes** have a **dot** over or under them. Play staccato notes short and separated.

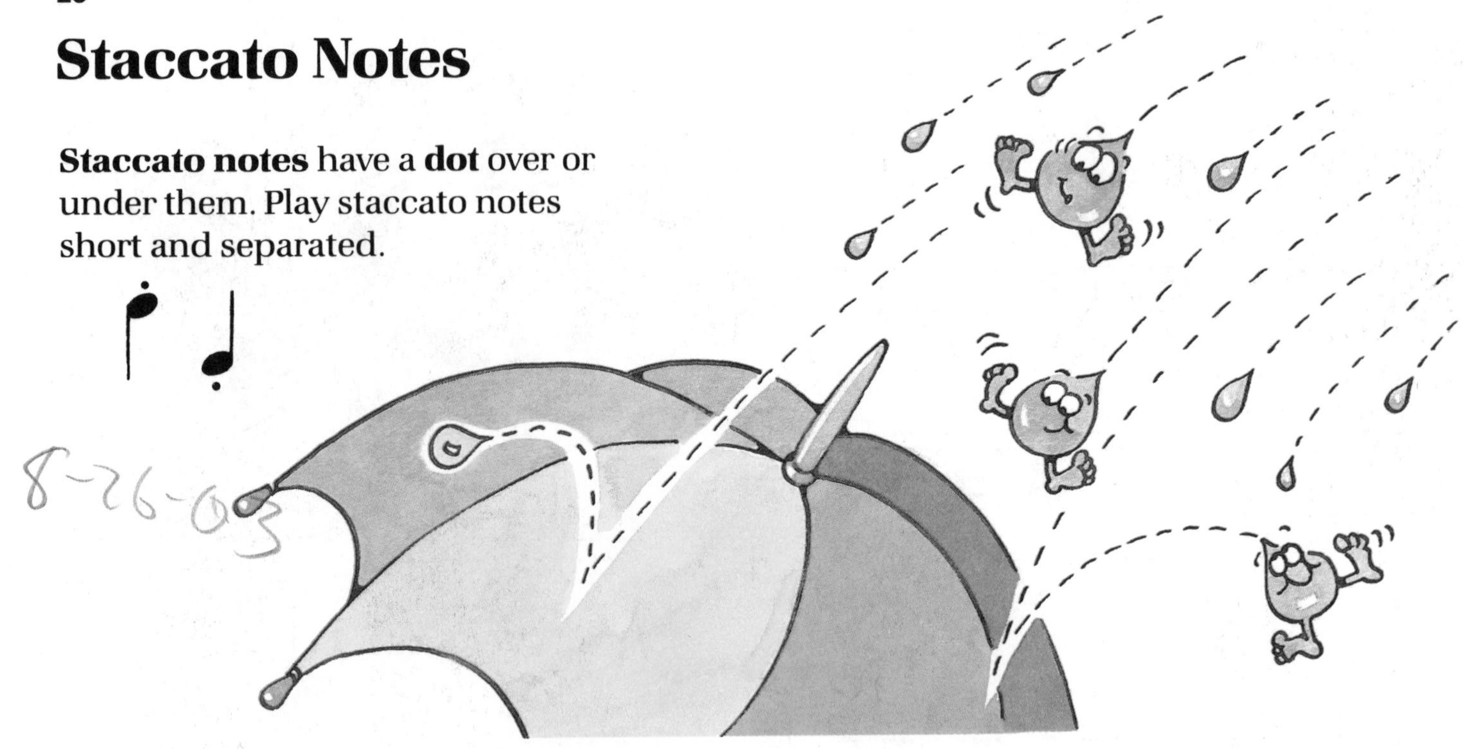


**60.** Draw dots over or under these notes. A dot goes **over** the note if the stem is down. A dot goes **under** the note if the stem is up. Play these staccato notes.

9-3-03

**61.** Draw dots over or under these harmonic intervals. Play these staccato notes.

*Use with page 32 of* Piano for the Young Beginner, *Primer B.*

9-3-03

**62.** Play these notes staccato.

## *Let's Jump*

## *Bouncing Balls*

# G Position

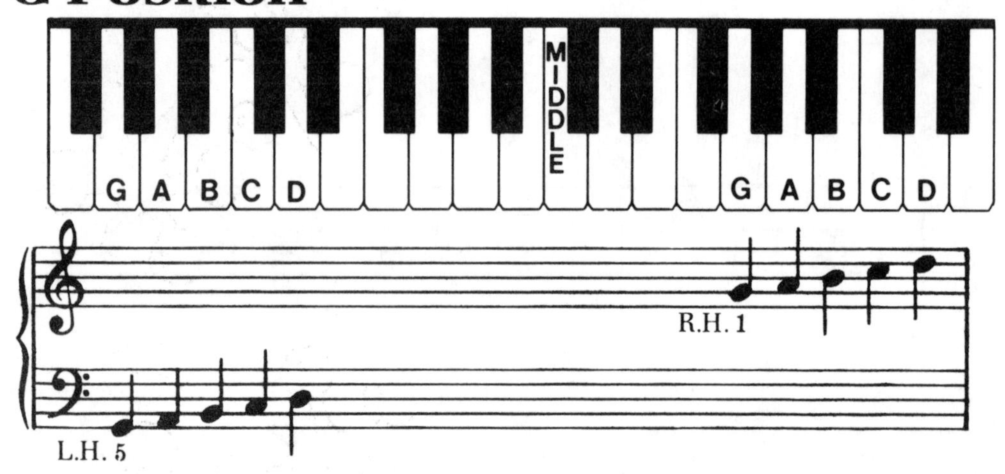


**63.** Draw quarter notes in the G position. Play and name these notes.

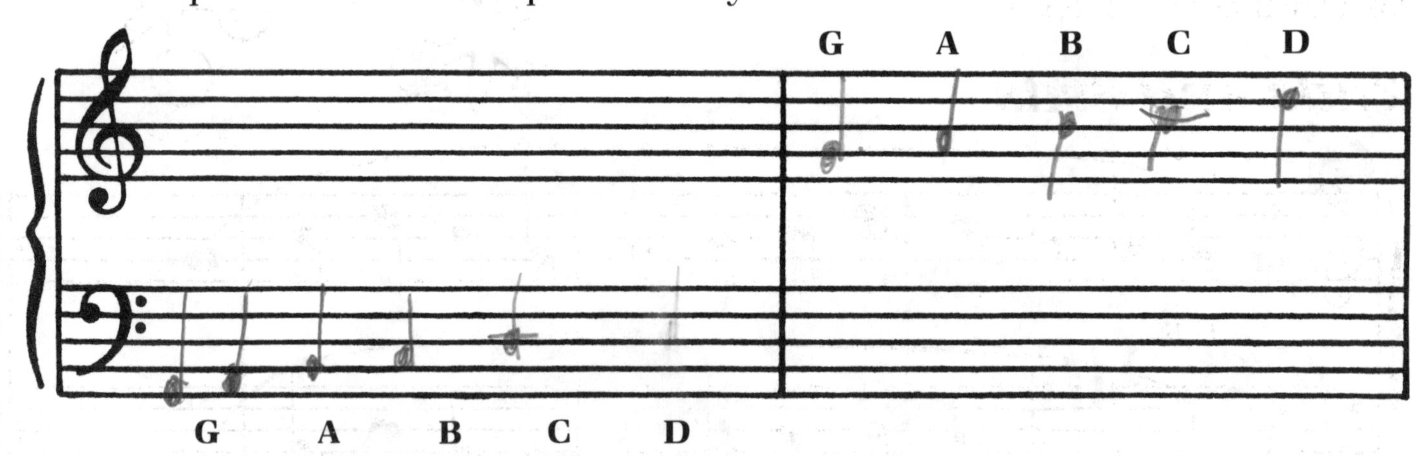


**64.** Write the names of these melodic intervals. Play them.

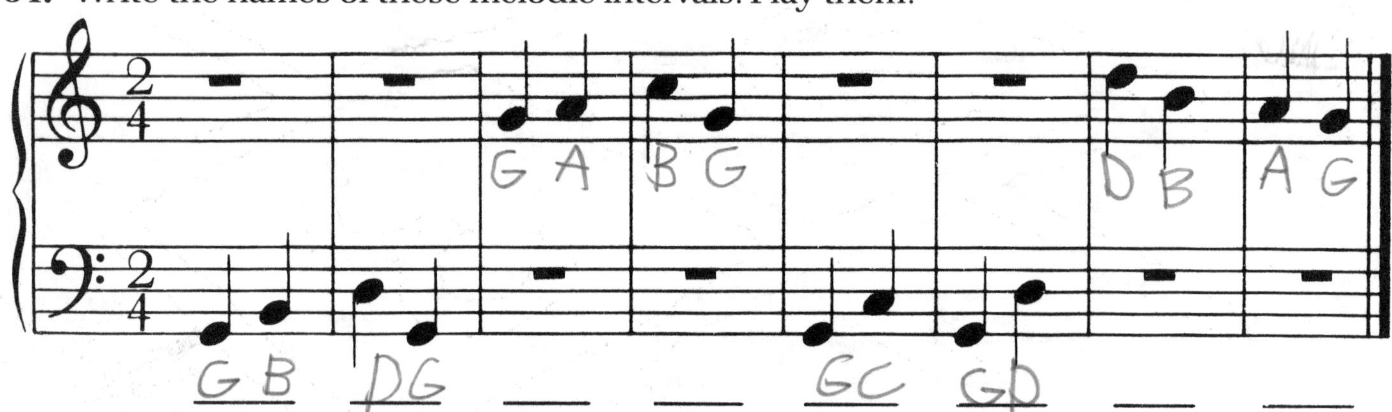

**65.** Write the names of these harmonic intervals. Play them.

66. Play these notes legato.
2nds and 3rds
1
f–p
5
Hopscotch
1
f–p
1
5

9-16-03

# Half Rest

A **half rest** lasts for the value of a half note.

Half note = 2 counts

Half rest = 2 counts

**67.** Fill in the first two half rests, then draw four more.
Draw the half rests sitting on the **3rd line**.

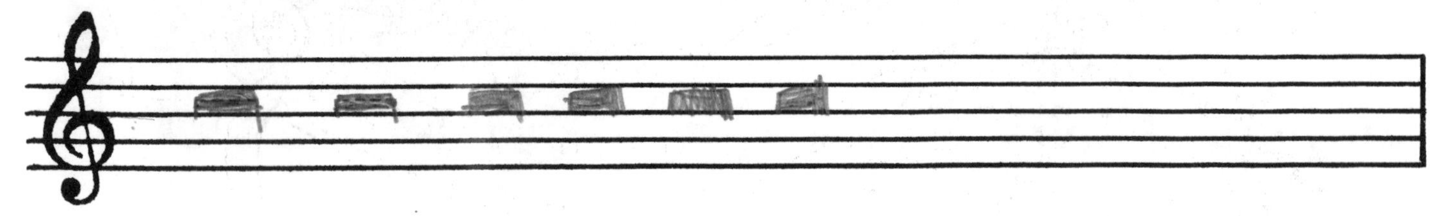

**68.** Draw half rests to complete the correct number of beats in each measure.

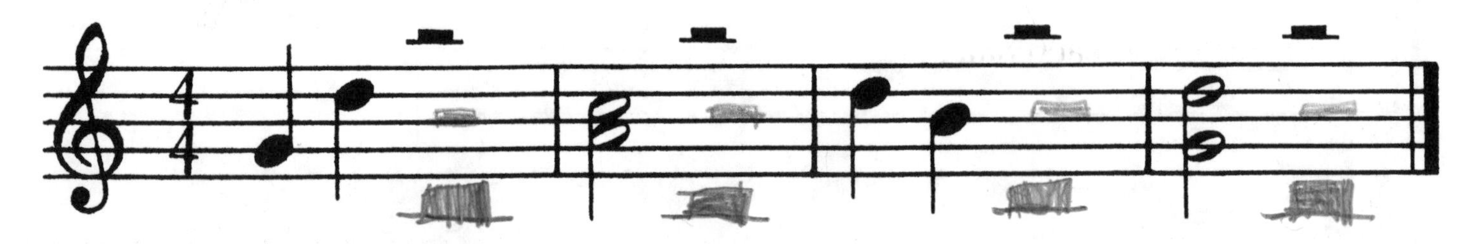

**69.** Draw half rests to complete the correct number of beats in each measure.

**70.** Draw half rests to complete the correct number of beats in each measure.

**71.** Rest 2 counts for each half rest.

## *Give Me a Rest!*

9-23-03

# Flat Sign

The **flat sign** before a note means to play the next key to the **left**.

**72.** Trace the first two flat signs, then draw four more.
First draw a straight line down.
Next, draw a heavy curved line.

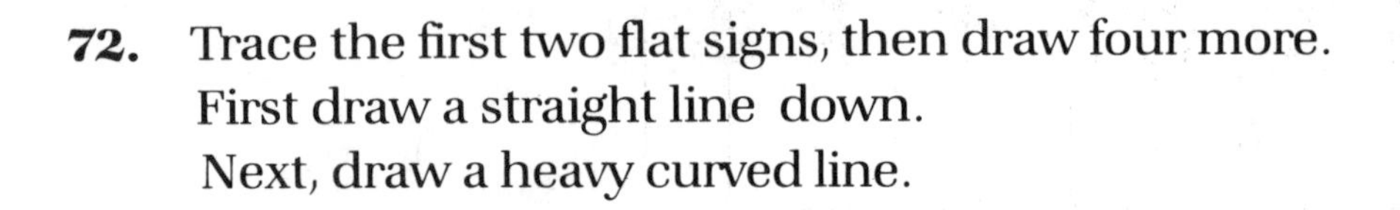

The "round" part of the flat is placed

on a **line** or in a **space**.

**73.** Draw a flat before each note. Play and name these notes.

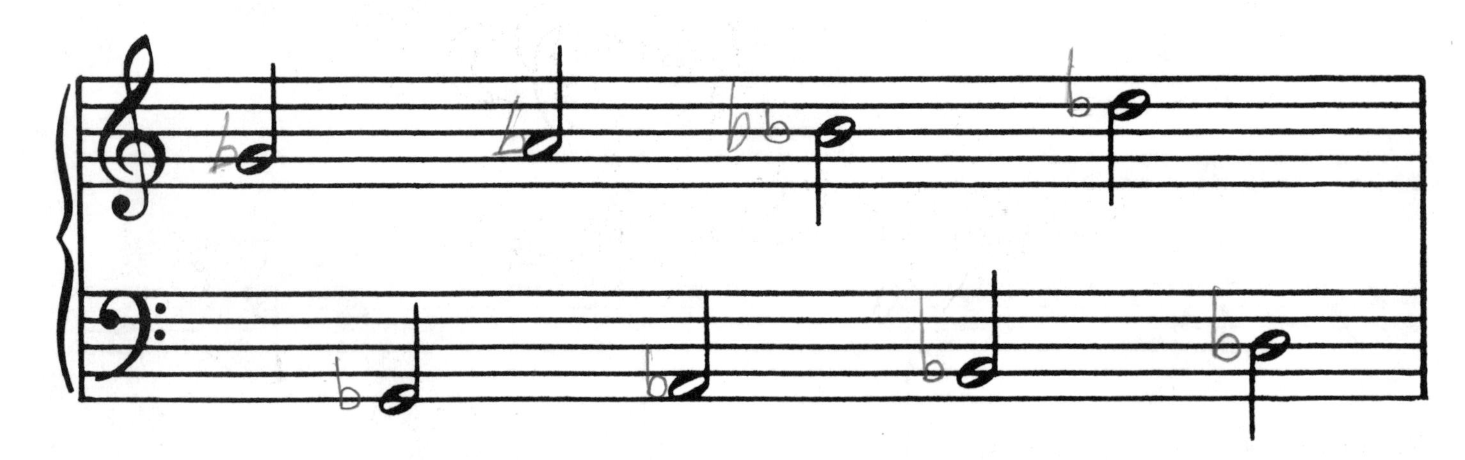

**74.** Draw a flat before each note with a ♭ sign over or under it.
Play and name these notes.

**75.** Write the names of these flat keys. Play them.

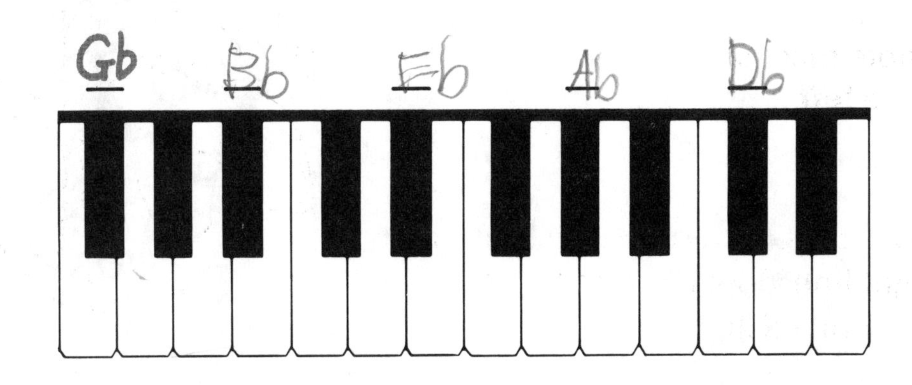


The flat sign lasts for the **whole** measure.

**76.** Remember to play B♭ again in each measure where B♭ is used.

## *In Outer Space*

*Use with page 41 of* Piano for the Young Beginner, *Primer B*.

77. Play these notes staccato.
Let's Rock!
f–p

*Use with pages 42-43 of* Piano for the Young Beginner, *Primer B.*

78. Lift your R.H. at the end of each slur on count 4.
Beaded Moccasins
legato
f
Staccato

# Review

**1.** Name these notes.

**2.** Add a beam to these pairs of notes to form eighth notes.

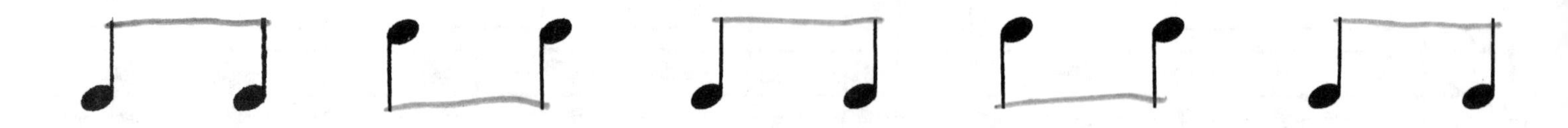

**3.** Name these notes.

**4.** ***f*** means ______________________ (loud, soft).

***p*** means ______________________ (loud, soft).

**5.** Name these **melodic** intervals.

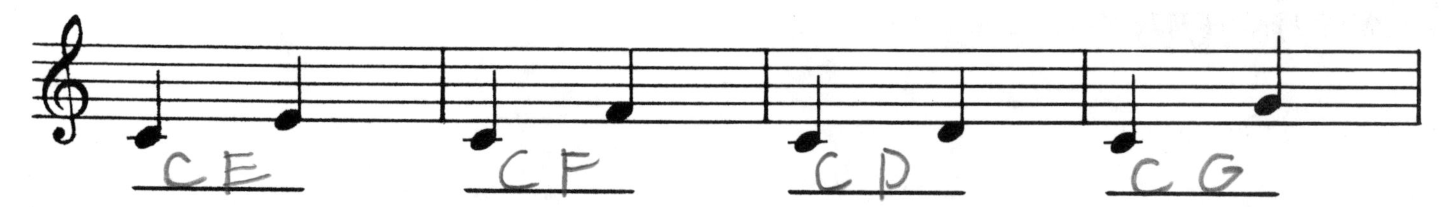


**6.** Name these **harmonic** intervals.

**7.** Draw a slur **over** these notes.

Draw a slur **under** these notes.

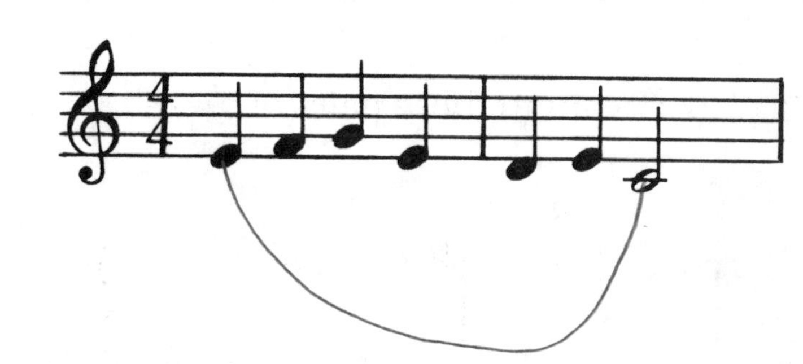

**8.** Draw a tie **under** these pairs of notes.

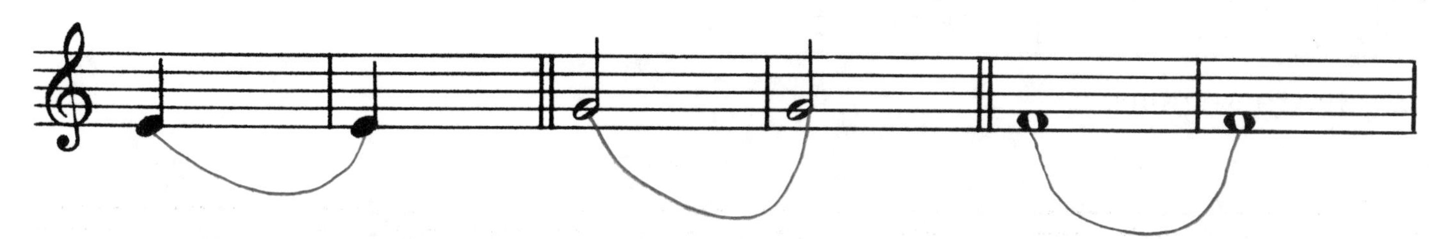

**9.** Draw a tie **over** these pairs of notes.

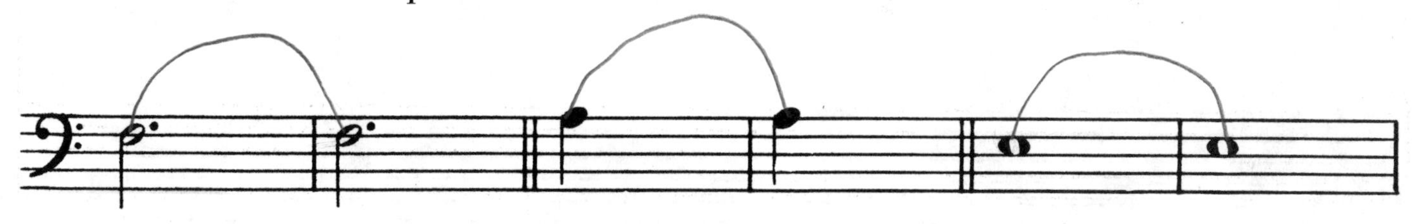

**10.** Name these rests.

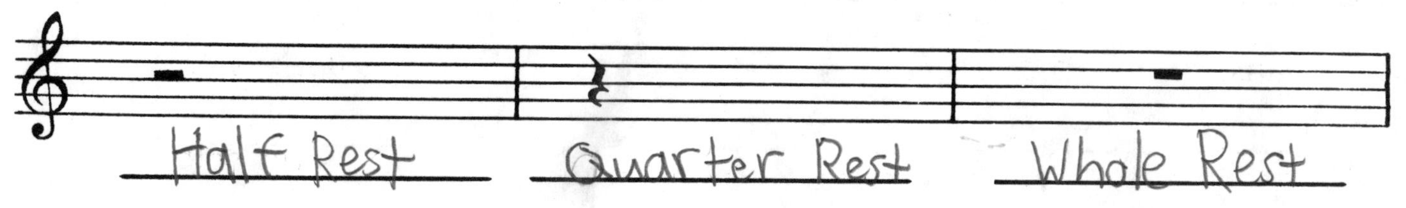

11. This sign ♯ is called a sharp sign.
It means to play the next key to the right.

12. This sign ♭ is called a flat sign.
It means to play the next key to the left.

13. These notes are played leggato.

14. These notes are played staccatto.

15. Name these notes.

G B C G B D A C D A